For Jasper
from Ocean x

published by
PENIARTH

www.**peniarth**.cymru

NATURE'S NASTIES

book 1
spring & summer

For my adorable granddaughter, Aminta Jane

© Text: Carol Barratt, 2018
© Design: Peniarth,
University of Wales Trinity Saint David, 2018

Illustrations by Ocean Hughes

Published in 2018 by Peniarth.

University of Wales Trinity Saint David asserts its moral right
under the Copyright, Designs and Patents Act, 1988 to be identified
respectively as author and illustrator of this work.

Contents

Spot the spider on every page.

I'm Meggie Mouse. Look out for me.

Prologue

In an old stone mill-house in the Welsh countryside, a boy called Tomos is staying with his grandparents. He loves to hear the stories that his grandmother tells him. Stories about animals, birds, trees and plants.

This book is a collection of his favourite stories featuring Morgan the donkey.

He asks his grandmother, "Are there really nasty things in nature?"

She answers, "Oh yes, I call them 'Nature's Nasties'. But actually some of them are quite amazing."

Who is Morgan?

Morgan is a descendant of the Penclawdd donkeys on the Gower coast, South Wales.

There was a time when these donkeys used to help the cockle-pickers carry the cockles on the flat donkey carts.

In the early evenings Morgan tells all the animals nearby to gather round his stable near the mill-house. Donkeys are very curious and very nosy!

Some of Morgan's friends

Sir Oswald Owl

A bit of a show-off.
He is wise and clever.

The Trio of Rabbits

Three rabbits who listen a lot
and giggle a lot.

Millie Moorhen

Usually on her own.
Her feet are rather large.

Phil Pheasant

Rather lazy and plump,
but he has beautiful feathers.

Wilberforce Weasel

A master-spy who is always snooping
around. He's a bit of a know-it-all.

Meggie Mouse

Very sweet but she
worries a lot.

Um! How did
that spider
get here?

Story 1: The Cuckoo
Early one evening in early spring

Morgan the Donkey says, "What a nasty bird the **cuckoo** is! I saw her lay her egg in another bird's nest. She then **pushed** out one of the eggs that was already there. She then flew off before the real owners of the nest returned."

Phil Pheasant says, "I could never do anything as nasty as that."

The trio of rabbits say, "**Oooh,** Morgan! The cuckoo makes such a lovely 'cuck-oo, cuck-oo' call as it sings. Is it really nasty? Sir Oswald Owl will know. He's **SO** clever."

A woodpecker joins in and says, "I think my sound is much more interesting. I make a lovely **knock-knock** drumming sound as I tap my beak on a tree. I'd rather drum than sing!"

Sir Oswald Owl says, "The cuckoo is too **lazy** to make its own nest. The cuckoo chick always hatches first and tips all the other bird eggs out of the nest. What a nasty thing to do! The poor parents have no idea that the new chick isn't their chick. It soon grows bigger than they are! They just keep feeding it and feeding it."

Phil Pheasant says, "Um, I thought I was lazy!"

10

But the cuckoo really does have a lovely call. It tells us that spring has arrived.

Story 2: The Water Shrew
Early one evening in spring

Morgan the Donkey says, "I saw a **water shrew** this morning, coming out of a hole by the stream. Maybe it had spotted our spring watercress beds and thought what a good place to hide. Suddenly it made a loud squeak and dived into the water to find some food. Maybe it had spotted some water beetles or tiny fish. I must say that a water shrew is **very smelly**. And someone told me that it spits?"

Millie Moorhen, who is always on her own, says, "I thought **my feet** were big, but the water shrew's feet are enormous."

The trio of rabbits say, "**Oooh, Morgan!** Does a water shrew really spit? Sir Oswald Owl will know. He's **SO** clever."

13

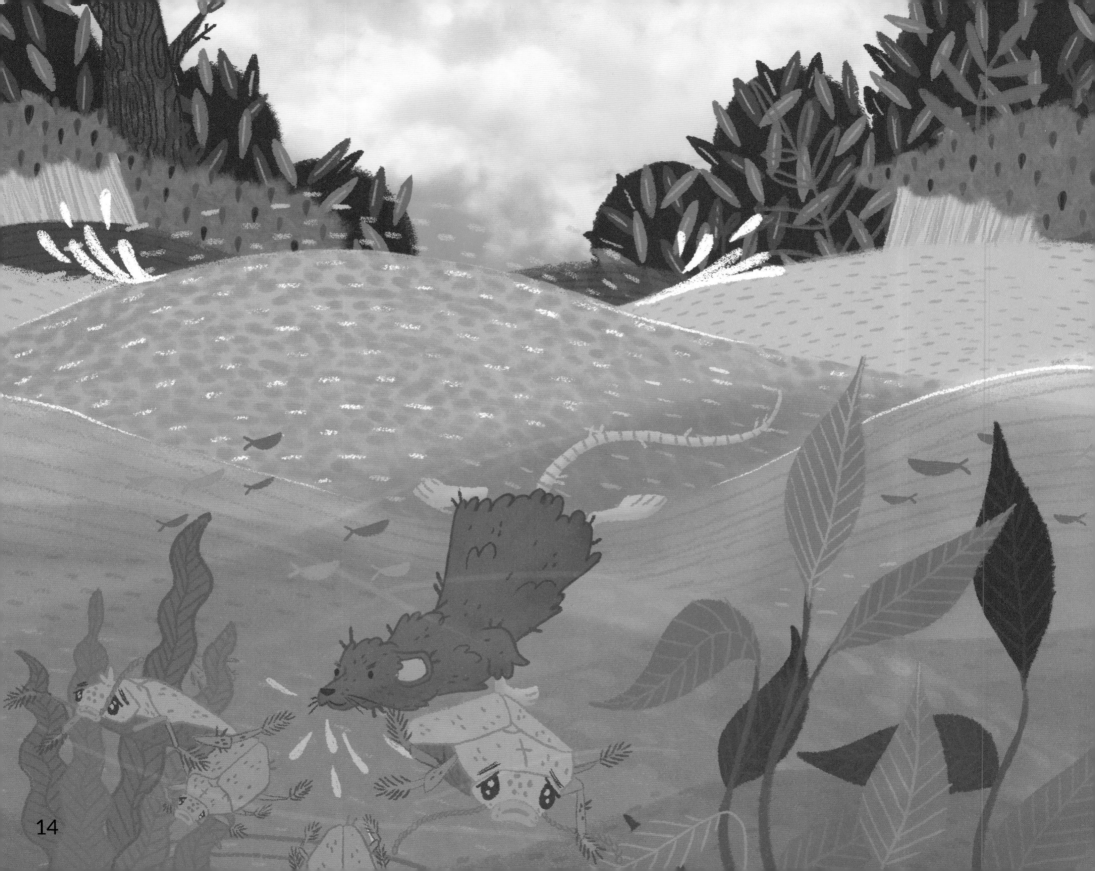

14

Sir Oswald Owl says, "Water shrews are **very shy**. They prefer to hide most of the time. Some of my owl friends have been known to eat them. Not me, of course! This furry creature spits a horrid liquid to **stun** its prey before killing it. Sometimes it even kills a fish that's **bigger** than he is! He just spits at it first! But the water shrew isn't really nasty. It's the spitting that's nasty."

Phil Pheasant says, "I know I'm lazy, I know I'm too heavy to fly very far, but at least I don't spit!"

Story 3: The Pike
Early one evening in spring

Morgan the Donkey says, "Our friend Jenny Swan flew to a nearby lake this morning. She had heard that a group of swans had landed there. You know how nosy she is! She wanted to check them out. Imagine her surprise when she saw a **large fish**, with a pointed head and a nasty grin on its face, coming towards her."

"It was a **pike**. She knew that pike like to **bite!** Although she knew that it probably wouldn't bite her, she didn't like the look of its nasty face at all. Hastily she returned to the safety of our pond. Phew!"

The trio of rabbits say, "**Oooh,** Morgan! Sir Oswald Owl will know all about pike. He's **so** clever."

Jenny told me that a group of swans is called 'A whiteness of swans'.

17

Sir Oswald Owl says, "Yes, pike can look **really scary**. And they can **bite**. A pike can even grow to the size of a small bed! Fishermen love to fish for pike as they are fun to watch. They are real **acrobats** in the water. Usually they are put back in the water when caught. But in some parts of the world, humans eat the larger ones. There are lots of stories about pike eating quite large animals like ducklings and voles, and even eating other pike!"

Wilberforce Weasel the master-spy, who happens to be passing by, splutters: "If ever **I** spot a pike, I'll tell it not to show its nasty face round here!"

Story 4: The Adder
Early one evening in late spring

Morgan the Donkey says, "After I'd had my hooves clipped at midday, I suddenly spotted a **snake**. It was wriggling through the grass near our pond. I noticed its zigzag stripes. Do you think it was poisonous?"

Phil Pheasant says, lazily, "I saw it too. Um, I nearly pecked it!"

The trio of rabbits say, "**Oooh**, Morgan! Maybe Sir Oswald saw the snake? He can tell us about it. He's **SO** clever."

Sir Oswald Owl says, "Yes, I saw a snake this afternoon as it stopped to **sunbathe** in the late spring sunshine. It was an **adder**. It uses its venomous bite to stun the live animal it is about to kill for food. That food includes mice, voles, and frogs."

Help! I don't want an adder to see me!

"Adders like to be left alone and are quite **shy**. Humans are only bitten if they try to catch one. For humans it's quite painful and I'm told it's best to let a doctor look at the bite."

Story 5: Slugs

Early one evening in early summer

Morgan the Donkey says to a badger who is strolling by: "What is the point of **slugs**? All they do is eat all the vegetables and flowers. Tomos' grandfather is always complaining about the slugs eating the plants that grow in his garden. Ugh, nasty, slimy things!"

The badger says, "I **love** to eat fat slugs as a special treat. I don't think they're at all nasty. They're yummy! Makes a change from eating earthworms. The **black slug** is a particular favourite of mine. Even foxes like an occasional meal of slugs."

The trio of rabbits say, "**Oooh**, Morgan! Sir Oswald Owl will know all about slugs. He's **so** clever."

Sir Oswald Owl says, "Ah yes, slugs. One of nature's nasties! **Gardeners hate slugs** and are always thinking up different ways of getting rid of them. But lots of animals and birds love to eat slugs. For example, ducks, chickens, snakes, song thrushes..."

A nearby toad interrupts and shouts out loudly, "**I love slugs**. Tell the gardeners not to get rid of all of them. Leave some for me!"

PE SLUGS
PEST CONTROL
GARDEN PESTS : SLUGS
SAVE YOUR GARDEN
KILL SLUGS

26

Millie Moorhen, who is always on her own, tries to join in the conversation: "Some slugs eat **worms** and this is such a pity, as worms do so much good in gardens."

Slugs always leave a nasty, slimy trail. But I think this looks nice and shiny and silvery.

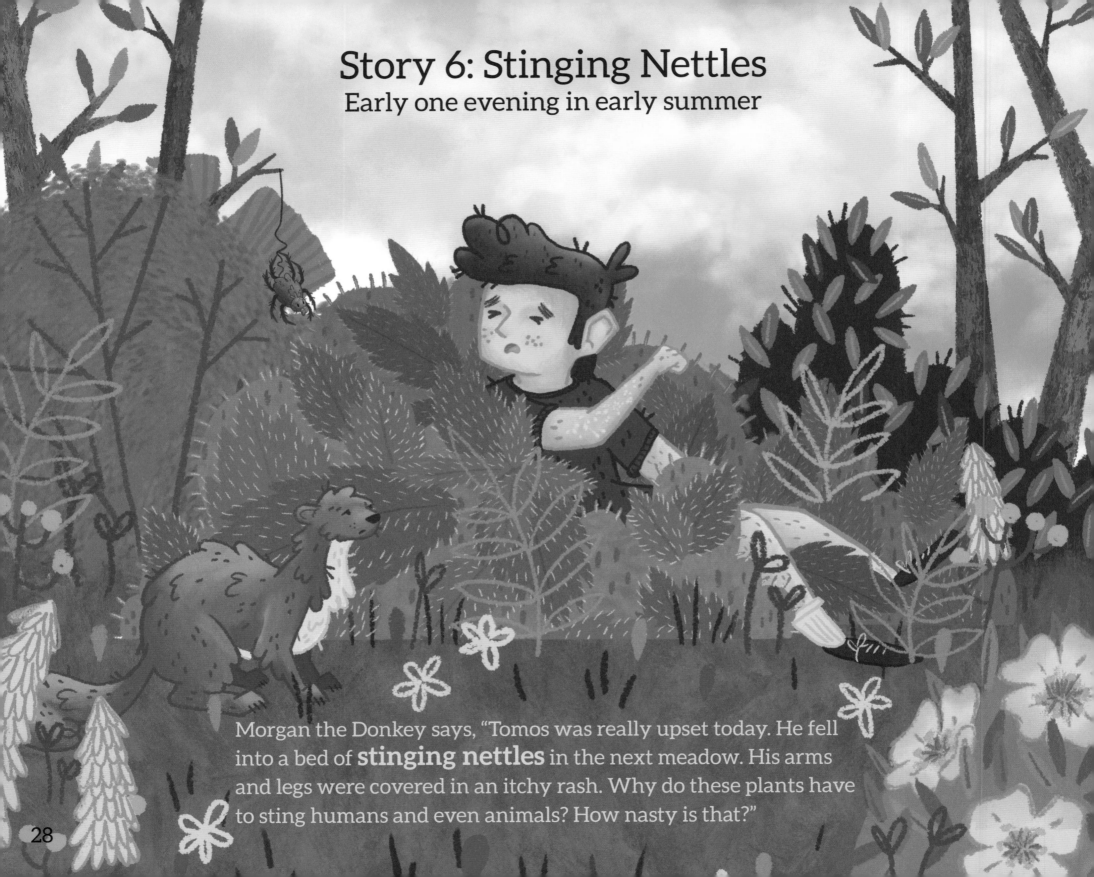

Story 6: Stinging Nettles
Early one evening in early summer

Morgan the Donkey says, "Tomos was really upset today. He fell into a bed of **stinging nettles** in the next meadow. His arms and legs were covered in an itchy rash. Why do these plants have to sting humans and even animals? How nasty is that?"

Wilberforce Weasel the master-spy, who happens to be passing by, says, "Umph! Tomos should look where he's going."

The trio of rabbits say, "**Oooh**, Morgan! Sir Oswald Owl will know all about stinging nettles. He's **SO** clever."

Sir Oswald Owl says, "Poor Tomos. Stinging nettles have a useful sting so that grazing **animals** don't fancy **eating** them. But insects can move between the stinging hairs of the nettles without being stung. A nettle patch is always full of **hairy caterpillars**."

"Boiled nettle leaves are also very useful in herbal **medicine** to make nettle soup and nettle tea. Tomos' grandmother often drinks **nettle tea** for her arthritis."

Tomos is fine now. His grandmother found some dock leaves and rubbed them in to his stings to dull the pain and cool his skin.

31

Story 7: Jellyfish
Early one evening in summer

Morgan the Donkey says, "This morning a heron told me that as he was flying over Limeslade Bay, he saw a huge dead **jellyfish** lying on the sand. It had obviously been **washed up** by the sea. He said it looked just like a nasty blob of jelly. Ugh!"

Wilberforce Weasel the master-spy, who happens to be passing by, says, "Mm! Maybe the recent **hot weather** means more jellyfish are swimming to Wales?"

He then says, smugly, to anyone who is listening, "A group of jellyfish is called 'A bloom of jellyfish'. Did any of you know that?"

The trio of rabbits ignore Wilberforce and say, "**Oooh**, Morgan! Let's ask Sir Oswald Owl about jellyfish. He's **SO** clever."

Sir Oswald Owl says, "It was probably a **barrel jellyfish**. It looks just like a see-through dustbin lid over a cauliflower! It's one of the **largest** jellyfish seen in Great Britain. It's quite **harmless** though. Not much of a sting. Or it could have been a **moon jellyfish** or even a **lion's mane jellyfish**. Jellyfish like to eat very tiny shrimp-like creatures. But who or what likes to eat jellyfish?! Hardly anything except **sea turtles** or, occasionally, sea birds."

Millie Moorhen, who is always on her own, says, "I heard Tomos' grandmother telling him, '**Never touch** a jellyfish just in case it's one with a **powerful sting**. But if one does sting you in Britain, it's a bit like a nettle sting. Nasty but not dangerous.'"

Story 8: Giant Hogweed
Early one evening in summer

Morgan the Donkey says, "This afternoon I heard Tomos' grandfather telling Farmer Cowley that they must be on the lookout for a nasty plant called **giant hogweed**. He said it spreads like billy-o and loves river banks. Farmer Cowley nodded knowingly and told him that it looks a bit like cow parsley but can grow to more than three metres tall."

"Apparently these plants were brought over here from other countries by humans who thought that they would make lovely ornamental plants in their gardens. Silly humans! But why are these plants so **dangerous**?"

The trio of rabbits say, "**Oooh**, Morgan! I'm sure Sir Oswald Owl will have heard about giant hogweed. He's **SO** clever."

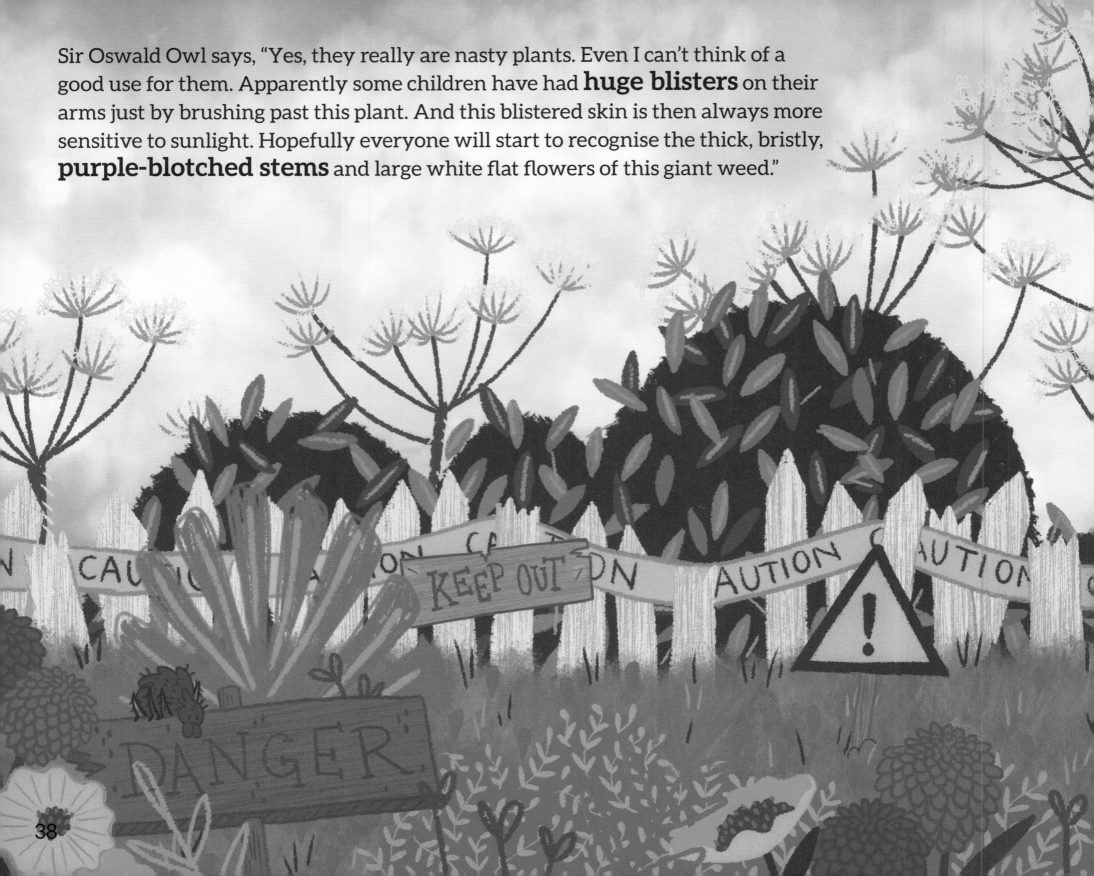

Sir Oswald Owl says, "Yes, they really are nasty plants. Even I can't think of a good use for them. Apparently some children have had **huge blisters** on their arms just by brushing past this plant. And this blistered skin is then always more sensitive to sunlight. Hopefully everyone will start to recognise the thick, bristly, **purple-blotched stems** and large white flat flowers of this giant weed."

KEEP OUT

CAUTION

AUTION

AUTION

DANGER

Wilberforce Weasel the master-spy, who happens to be passing by, says, "Let's make sure we don't get any around here. I'll keep a lookout."

39

Story 9: Flies
Early one evening in summer

Morgan the Donkey says, "Farmer Cowley's cows and sheep in the next field have been complaining all day about the **flies** that keep buzzing around them. Flies really bother them. They really bother **me** as well!"

"I know that flies can give animals illnesses. Humans don't like them either, as they land on their food, spreading dirt and germs. What is the point of nasty flies?"

The trio of rabbits say, "**Oooh**, Morgan! Sir Oswald Owl will know all about flies. He's **SO** clever."

Sir Oswald Owl says, "Flies can seem pointless and yes, they can even **spread diseases**. But they are also quite **useful**. They feed on **dead creatures**. Imagine how many dead animals killed on the road would be left lying around if it weren't for flies eating them? But it's a good job that the flies are then eaten by frogs, lizards, dragonflies, spiders and some types of birds..."

Wilberforce Weasel the master-spy, who happens to be passing by, interrupts and says, importantly, "Pesky flies! I must look into this. The sheep, the cows, and even Morgan, are so fed up with flies."

Phil Pheasant adds, "Mm! Yes, they can be useful in more ways than one. I once heard Tomos' grandfather reciting an old saying that goes like this:

If a fly lands on your nose,
Swat it till it goes.
If the fly then lands again,
It will bring back heavy rain."

That can't be true!

43

Story 10: Burrs
Early one evening in late summer

Morgan the Donkey says, "Nasty **burrs**! At this time of year they are **sticking** to the fur of many of my animal friends. They really irritate their skin. Even those two little white furry dogs that live at the mill-house often get them stuck to their legs and feet. I suppose there must be a reason for such horrid prickly things, but I can't think what it is."

A fox crouching nearby says, "Ugh! Drat these burrs."

Millie Moorhen, who is always on her own, says to Morgan: "Oh, don't let that fox see me! I hope he's already had his dinner! I hope he's not still hungry!"

The trio of rabbits say, "**Oooh**, Morgan! Sir Oswald Owl can tell us all about these prickly balls. He's **SO** clever."

Sir Oswald Owl says, "A burr is a prickly **seedcase** that has tiny hooks or teeth. They may seem nasty, but it's a very clever way for the plant to carry seeds to another place. They can even get attached to car tyres and go on long journeys!"

"I once heard Tomos' grandfather say crossly, as he tried to pull some burrs off his jumper, 'The man who invented Velcro must have been thinking of burrs at the time!'"

Stick around for Book 2!

Quiz

Here are some questions to see if you can remember facts from this book.

1. What creature looks like a see-through dustbin lid over a cauliflower?

2. What bird is too lazy to build its own nest?

3. What small, nasty, black things eat dead creatures?

4. What small animal that lives in a hole near streams or rivers is very smelly?

5. What has zigzag stripes and slithers through grass?

6. Who loves to eat black slugs for dinner?

7. What kind of leaf is soothing when it's rubbed on nettle stings?

8. Name an animal that eats flies.

9. What is a group of swans called?

10. What bird or animal has a way of telling us that spring has arrived?

11. What plant can give you huge blisters?

12. What animal lives in a hole and spits at its prey?

13. What fish are known as 'acrobats in the water'?

14. Do earthworms do good or bad things in a garden?

15. What area in a field is always full of hairy caterpillars?

16. What is a group of jellyfish called?

17. What seedcase sticks like Velcro?

18. What giant weed has large white flat flowers?

19. What fish can even eat ducklings and voles?

20. What bird makes a drumming sound on a tree?

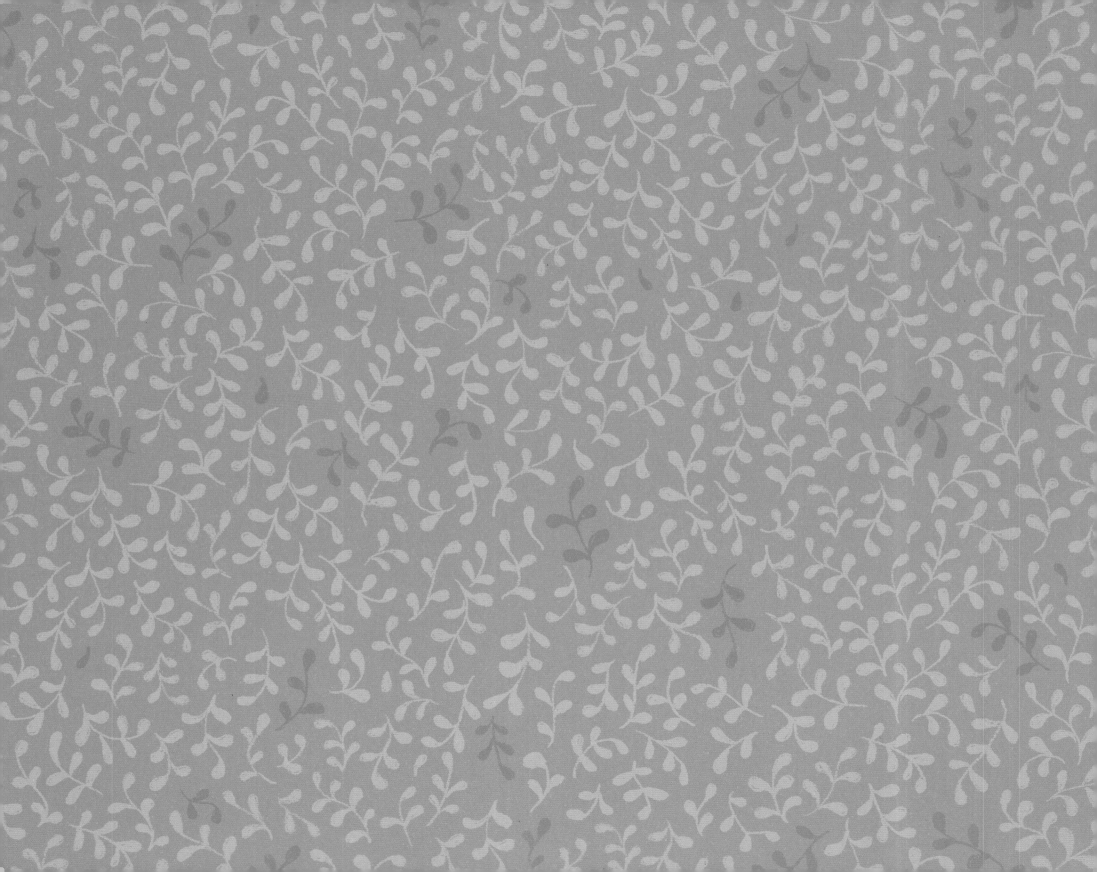